Praise for *The Mis*

These two academics-tu..

hearts and the heart of God like few others. In *The Missing Commandment: Love Yourself*, they place emotional and spiritual health on a solid foundation of love—for God, for others, and for self.

—Gary W. Moon, MDiv, PhD, executive director, Dallas Willard Center for Christian Spiritual Formation; author, *Apprenticeship with Jesus*

For those who long to be awakened to their true identity in Christ, these pages speak from the heart and will clearly lead readers toward finding peace and wholeness in him.

—Kimberly Powers, cofounder, Walk the Talk Youth Ministries, Inc.; speaker; author, *Escaping the Vampire: Desperate for the Immortal Hero*

This is the Original Good News, aimed at the lies we've been telling ourselves about us. The Basels display with winsome confidence the astonishing love of the Father, which alone allows us to love ourselves honestly, deeply, and wonderfully.

—John Lynch, Bruce McNicol, and Bill Thrall, bestselling coauthors, *The Cure, Bo's Café,* and *The Ascent*

Jerry and Denise do a masterful job of helping readers find a pathway of healing from the self-hatred and low self-esteem that many have embraced for a lifetime.

—Roger and Gerri Taylor, cofounders, Places in the Father's Heart, Inc.; coauthors, *Our Glory Stories* and *The Heart of Marriage*

The message of the Father's love is incredibly important. Jerry and Denise Basel possess a keen awareness of the need for ministry in this area, not only because they have extensive counseling experience but also because they themselves live close to the heart of God.

—Billy Humphrey, director, International House of Prayer Atlanta; author, *To Know Him*

A truthful, profound, and appropriate treatment of a fundamental issue affecting all of our lives. You will find real truth and healing in its pages. Be warned—it can change your life!

—Rev. Alfred Ells, MC, executive director,
Leaders That Last Ministries; counselor; consultant; author,
One-Way Relationships and *Leaders That Last*

Written from the compassionate view of seasoned counselors, *The Missing Commandment: Love Yourself* carefully guides us through the various issues of life and into the Father's waiting arms.

—Ed Piorek, Father Loves You Ministries; speaker; author,
Father Loves You and *The Central Event*

To love ourselves in a healthy way is simply coming into agreement with how God already loves us. Jerry and Denise have done an amazing job of communicating this simple yet profound truth.

—Barry Adams, Father Heart Communications; speaker;
author, *Father's Love Letter*

Whenever I have a chance to review a book, I ask myself, "Would I use this material in my ministry?" In the case of this book the answer is, absolutely. I believe God is going to use the message of this book to set many people free.

—Ken Nash, teaching pastor, Cornerstone Church,
Grand Rapids, Michigan

Jerry and Denise Basel reveal the deep frontiers of recovering the lost life of the heart. This book is not just information: it is a guided path to healing, restoration, wholeness, forgiveness of self, and freedom from shame.

—Tom Colwell, director of pastoral care, Credential Holders and Pastors,
Pentecostal Assemblies of Canada, Western Ontario District;
cofounder, Men of Life Ministries, Canada

I am so excited about this book that words fail me. I don't think I've read anything like it: personal and didactic at the same time in a very easy flow. I can see it transforming lives. I can't wait for it to come out because I'll buy it in bulk.

—Dr. Bill Curnow, L.I.F.E. Coaching International, Wyoming, Michigan

A powerful book . . . [full of] practical and thought-provoking wisdom from two skilled counselors. These pages graciously invite the reader to discover and practice self-love and to truly understand, embrace, and rest in the love of God the Father.

—A. J. Gregory, author, *Messy Faith* and *Silent Savior*; writer/collaborator on *Nowhere but Up* with Pattie Mallette

Jerry and Denise brilliantly uncover the issues that are hiding in the dark corners of our story. This book will give you permission to love yourself the way that God loves you. Though it may feel selfish, it's the most unselfish thing you can do.

—Pattie Mallette, New York Times bestselling author of *Nowhere but Up*

Finally I have a single, solid book to give to clients which can help them get to the real issue under the issues. We all need to know the Father's deep love for us experientially in order to . . . love and live fully because our hearts are fully convinced we are lovable, worthy, valuable human beings. I heartily recommend this book.

—Lorraine Turbyfill, M.Ed., licensed professional counselor; certified sex therapist

A gem for every follower of Christ, especially those called to assist others on the road to inner healing. If you're a pastor, you should read this book for personal reflection and deeper discovery of God's amazing grace. This book will also become a powerful tool in the hands of your church members. Your church will have a greater measure of God's love to offer a hurting, broken, and lost world.

—Greg Mayo, senior pastor, Cornerstone Church of Augusta

This book touches the deep places of the heart, filling in a missing piece of spiritual formation that has largely been neglected by the church. If you seek a resource to help you experience the Father's love in a deep and fresh way—then this is it!

—Rick Mailloux, lead pastor, Pequea Brethren in Christ Church,
Lancaster, Pennsylvania

When you read *The Missing Commandment: Love Yourself*, you need to be ready for open-heart surgery. As I read, I felt the invisible hands of grace soothe the pain and numbness out of my heart. If you want to live from the whole of your heart and feel Jesus living through and in you, then this book is a must.

—Pablo Giacopelli, professional tennis coach on the WTA Tour;
author of *Holding On Loosely.*

In *The Missing Commandment: Love Yourself*, Jerry and Denise take you on a heart expedition that will help you discover who you really are—the glorious person God has created you to be and whom he truly loves.

—Gary Barkalow, founder, The Noble Heart; author,
It's Your Call: What Are you Doing Here

THE MISSING COMMANDMENT
LOVE YOURSELF

DVD STUDY GUIDE

THE MISSING
COMMANDMENT
LOVE
YOURSELF

DVD STUDY GUIDE

JERRY AND DENISE BASEL

HEART & LIFE
PUBLISHERS

The Missing Commandment: Love Yourself DVD Study Guide

Copyright © 2014 by Jerry and Denise Basel
All rights reserved.

Published by J & D Publications in Cleveland Georgia,
www.jerryanddenisebasel.com and by Heart & Life Publishers,
a division of Miles Media, LLC, in Grand Rapids, Michigan,
www.heartandlife.com.

ISBN:978-0-9839924-3-1

Unless otherwise noted, Scripture quotations are from The Message.
Copyright © 1993, 1994, 1995, 1996, 2000, 2001, 2002. Used by
permission of the Navpress Publishing Group.

Editor: Bob Hartig, www.thecopyfox.com
Cover design: jeffgiffordcreative.com
Author photo: Christa Wilson, Raebeam Photography
Interior design: Frank Gutbrod

Printed in the United States of America

CONTENTS

HOW TO USE THIS STUDY GUIDE

Well done! Purchasing this study guide shows that you have chosen to take a life-changing journey—one that will help you expose the lies that have held you captive and replace them with the truth of who God really is and who you really are. In the seven sessions that follow, you will discover how you can align your heart, thoughts, and emotions—and as a result, your life and relationships—with the Father's transforming love, not just for other people but for *you*. As you learn to love yourself the way God does, you will also grow in your capacity to love God and others better—freely and gladly, from your heart.

Designed for use with *The Missing Commandment: Love Yourself* DVD, this study guide will help you get the most out of every session. Each session includes the following components:

- **Introductory Scripture** reading from *The Message* (MSG) equips you with a solid biblical basis for the material that follows. You'll gain new insights into God's Word and its implications for your personal peace and growth as you discover the character of the Father's heart.

- **Overview** of the content will prepare you for the material that will be covered in-depth in the DVD.

- **Reading Assignment** correlates the session with key chapters in the book *The Missing Commandment: Love Yourself*, which you should read prior to viewing the video. While you can profit from the DVD and study guide by themselves, we *strongly advise* that you include the book as an integral part of the sessions. The insights and benefits you will gain from it cannot be overstated.

- **Video Session** begins by telling you which session to view and how long it lasts. Knowing the running time is particularly helpful if you are leading a small group. The session then moves into the video narrative, described in the following bullet.

- **Video Narrative** appears as a part of the video session. Different titles (e.g., "The Two Pegs," "Nesting Dolls: The Child Within," etc.) describe the content covered. Adapted from the script used in the DVD session, the narrative is designed to facilitate personal or small group review and reflection.

- **Prayer** is designed to help you take the material you've covered and present it to God. You can personalize the prayer to make it your own. The prayer creates space for you to connect heart-to-heart with the Father about your discoveries, thoughts, and emotions—because you're not on this journey alone. He's in it with you. He's trustworthy, present for you one hundred percent, hugely encouraging, and eager to help you grow and become who you truly are.

- **Questions and Exercises** can be used for individual processing and journaling. Most of these are simply questions. A few items will take you in a more active direction, but the goal is the same: to guide you in thinking deeply about how the material applies to you personally and to help you internalize what you've learned.

If you are using the DVD and study guide in a small group, consider which parts you are ready and willing to share with the group.

INTRODUCTION

Have you ever wondered why it sometimes seems so hard to live out of the freedom that Jesus came to give all who follow him? Have you wondered why it is difficult to experience—consistently—love, joy, and peace? Do you long for deeper, more meaningful relationships with others and with God, but you usually have to settle for less—sometimes much less?

No doubt there are many reasons for these struggles, but one significant factor often stays under the radar for many people: an inability to love themselves the way God does.

In our experience as counselors working with hundreds of clients over the past two decades, people's inability to love themselves is the most significant hindrance in their ability to love God and others and to walk in freedom and wholeness. When we love ourselves, we experience greater peace and joy in life, and we become better able to fulfill the destiny God places within us. This powerful truth and its implications for our lives inspired us to write the book *The Missing Commandment: Love Yourself—How Loving Yourself the Way God Does Can Bring Healing and Freedom to Your*

Life. It is the reason we have also produced our teaching DVD of the same title and this companion study guide.

It might seem that loving yourself is selfish. Aren't you supposed to "give preference to one another" (Rom. 12:10 NASB)? The problem comes when we try to love, care for, and give to others when we have little within us to offer them. Looking at it another way, when we are not loving ourselves the way God does, we cannot effectively love others that way either, and we also cannot fulfill the Greatest Commandment very well—namely, to love God with everything we've got. We further believe it is not possible to do a good job of keeping the foremost commandment, loving God, without fulfilling all of the next-greatest commandment, loving your neighbor as yourself.

As you work through this study guide and view the accompanying DVD, know that your goal is simply this: to come into full agreement with who God says you are and how he feels about you. Our prayer is that as you are able to do this, you will begin to experience more of the life that the Father has to give you.

LOVE GOD, LOVE SELF, LOVE OTHERS

When the Pharisees heard how he had bested the Sadducees, they gathered their forces for an assault. One of their religion scholars spoke for them, posing a question they hoped would show him up: "Teacher, which command in God's Law is the most important?"

Jesus said, "'Love the Lord your God with all your passion and prayer and intelligence.' This is the most important, the first on any list. But there is a second to set alongside it: 'Love others as well as you love yourself.' These two commands are pegs; everything in God's Law and the Prophets hangs from them."

(Matt. 22:34–40)

"It's who you are and the way you live that count before God. Your worship must engage your spirit in the pursuit of truth. That's the kind of people the Father is out looking for: those who are simply and honestly themselves before him in their worship. God is sheer being itself—Spirit. Those who worship him must do it out of their very being, their spirits, their true selves, in adoration."
(John 4:23–24)

Overview

In session 1, we introduce the often overlooked, underrated, and misunderstood command to love ourselves. We often quote the saying, "Love what God loves, hate what God hates, and don't get them mixed up." Unfortunately, many Christ-followers struggle with the exact opposite: hating what God loves—themselves.

We conclude this section with "Kara's Story": one woman's account of how God transformed her self-loathing into a life-giving new awareness of her identity as God's "Beloved."

Reading Assignment

In the book *The Missing Commandment: Love Yourself*, read the introduction (pp. 1–4) and chapter 1, "Love What God Loves," (pp. 5–22).

Video Session

On the teaching DVD, watch session 1, "Love God, Love Self, Love Others" (5:57). You can use the narrative script below for review and reflection. Highlight or make notes of any parts that stand out to you.

The Two Pegs

When we started The Father's Heart Ministry, the Scripture that was most important for us was, "Love the Lord your God with all your heart, with all your soul and with all your mind and all your strength." (Basically—love him with all you've got). "This is the first and most important command on any list."

But, Jesus continued, "There is a second that is set right alongside it: 'Love others as well as you love yourself.' These two commands are pegs mounted side by side, and everything in God's Law and the Prophets hangs from them." *Everything.*

Initially, our counseling ministry was tethered to the first commandment: to love the Lord your God with all your heart, soul, mind and strength. Part of our focus then was on sharing the heart of the Father—his compassion, tenderness, mercy, and loving correction for us. Along with that, we focused on healing the hearts of his children so that they had a whole heart to love him with.

Now, somewhere along the way, we realized that he shifted our eyes to the "second peg," and it wasn't the part of loving others—it was the part of how we had to love ourselves and then love others the same way. And you know what? If you think you are loving others but you're not that crazy about yourself—if you're hard and critical of yourself—then you can't really be loving others, including God.

Kara's Story

I never lost an opportunity to put myself down or make a derogatory comment about myself. Compliments were never met with a "Thank you." Instead, I quickly pointed out why the compliment-giver was wrong. I was sure that even God was disappointed in me—that I was his first mistake. That when he looked at me, he thought, "Oops, I forgot to give that one any talents at all!"

I confess I have a weakness for buying books. My shelves are full, but never, ever would I have picked up a book on learning to love myself. Crazy! Isn't that unbiblical? And so unnecessary! I wanted to learn to love God better. My family better. My neighbors better. Not myself! If Jerry and Denise had said early on in my journey that loving myself would be a critical component of healing, I probably would have sought out different counselors, concluding they were on the wrong track.

Thankfully, they lovingly and slowly pointed out how the lies I'd believed about myself grieved God. I had to stop tearing myself down and repeat his truth to myself. "Beloved" became a significant word for me early on. I struggled with even saying it, but slowly I came to embrace it. I tentatively accepted that God viewed me as Beloved. I can't tell you what a battle it's been to get to this point.

So why isn't learning to love yourself the most self-absorbed thing ever? One day it struck me that somehow in this process, I really had become a more loving person. I was quite taken aback. How had this happened? It seems the more grace I gave myself, the more willing I was to offer grace to others. The more tender I was with my own imperfections, the more natural it became to accept the mistakes of the people around me. As I started to view myself as God's Beloved, I began to see his image in the very people who would have irritated or annoyed me before. Don't misunderstand—this is still very much a work in progress! But that often-quoted verse, "Love your neighbor as yourself," has taken on new meaning.

I've learned that you can't chop out the second half of the verse and expect to do well at the first. In order to love your neighbor well, you really do have to learn to love yourself as God does—tenderly, completely, unfailingly.

I can actually say, "I am his Beloved!"

PRAYER

Father, I want to view myself the way you do—but do I? Maybe I do view myself the way I think you do, but therein lies the problem. Do I feel you're disappointed in me, or you're aloof, indifferent, or critical of me? Is that how I feel toward myself? I want to know the truth about how you really see me and how you feel about me, and I want to be in total agreement with that. I really do want to love myself and thus be able to love you and others more. Please help me with this, Lord. I need you. In Jesus' name, amen.

QUESTIONS AND EXERCISES

1. Do you find that you are the one who is hardest on yourself? Is your self-talk negative or grace-filled? Share examples from your life story.

2. In reference to 1 Corinthians 13, how do you respond to the following questions? Why or why not? Give examples of how your answers play out in your life.
   - Do I love myself?
   - Am I patient, gentle, and kind to myself?
   - Do I easily let go of my mistakes and wrongs?
   - Do I hold myself in contempt?
   - Do I continually doubt or shame or berate or condemn myself?
   - Do I trust myself?

3. Ponder this question in your heart: What would change for you if your perception of Emmanuel, "God with us," shifted from a general, God-is-everywhere perspective to a personal view of "God with *me*? God right next to me. Arm around me. Always. Never moving. Never changing. Never giving up on me. Loving me. *Always*." If your heart could see God in this manner, how might things be different for you?

4. Are there any parts of Kara's story that you relate to personally?

5. What do you believe God thinks and feels when he looks at you? Be real here.

6. Write a prayer or letter to God. What are you learning, wondering, or considering about how he sees you in comparison to how you see yourself? What do you need from him as it relates to loving yourself?

NOTES

THE ROLES WE PLAY

"I'm baptizing you here in the river, turning your old life in for a kingdom life. The real action comes next: The main character in this drama— compared to him I'm a mere stagehand—will ignite the kingdom life within you, a fire within you, the Holy Spirit within you, changing you from the inside out. He's going to clean house—make a clean sweep of your lives. He'll place everything true in its proper place before God; everything false he'll put out with the trash to be burned."
(Matt. 3:11–12)

Overview

In session 2, we (Jerry and Denise) share part of our personal stories about how our identities were shaped at a very early age. Both of us picked up roles in our homes that cost us part of our childhoods—roles we carried into adulthood, including our marriage, our relationships with others, and our relationship with God.

Reading Assignment

In the book *The Missing Commandment: Love Yourself*, read chapter 2, "But Wouldn't That Be Selfish?" (pp. 23–30).

Video Session

On the teaching DVD, watch session 2: "The Roles We Play" (4:54). You can use the narrative script below for your own review and reflection. Highlight or make notes of any parts that stand out to you.

The Journey

As Denise and I have walked through our own journeys of healing, we have had to ask ourselves many different questions, such as

- When did I learn to strive, to perform, to look and act a certain way in order to earn approval or avoid conflict?
- When did I start saying yes when I needed to say no?
- When did I begin hiding the real me because I felt inadequate, insecure, guilty, alone, unloved, self-contemptuous, and unable to measure up?

- When did I decide in my heart that I would never be weak, that I would always be in control, that I would never let anyone know I was hurting?

Finding answers to questions like these is a doorway into the journey of healing our hearts.

The Nice Guy: Jerry's Story

I was what many would consider a "nice guy." But in reality, my heart wasn't so nice. Because of some core deficits in my childhood, much of my love and care for others was driven by my own need for acceptance. I became a people-pleaser and a peace-keeper, and I learned early on to avoid conflict at all cost.

My identity was built on a core of lies, mainly about myself—the lies that say there is something inherently wrong, flawed, or defective about me. If you knew the real me, you wouldn't like me. I did not love or like myself, making it impossible for me to truly love others. Often I would do loving things, but my actions had the wrong motivation.

You can imagine how this worked in my marriage with Denise. For years she wanted more of my heart, but I was unable to give it. I couldn't be emotionally intimate with her because I didn't even know my own heart. As I began to let God pour his love into places within me that desperately needed it, I learned to love myself—especially my younger self.

Today I operate much more from my true, God-created self. I think Denise would agree that I am no longer a nice guy but a "real" guy—and she is very grateful for that! And so am I.

The Martyr: Denise's Story

I don't know exactly when, but sometime during my childhood, I began taking on the problems and burdens of others. I always befriended the underdog and the outcast. I read every book on the lives of the saints in our Catholic school library, and I was ready to lay down my life in order to deny myself and prefer others. There was just one huge missing piece: I didn't have a self to lay down.

Let me say that in another way: a child who gets lost in order to please others does not have anything to truly give away. I needed to find my true self—the identity God knit within me—before I could love others fully. Jesus never wavered in who he was. He had a self he could sacrifice for others. But I had made a martyr of myself before I even had a self to be martyred. And I did it in my own strength by trying to be "good."

P R A Y E R

Father, you are the God of truth, and I want to be true to who you say I am and live from that place. Reveal to me where I have taken on an identity—a role—that is not coming from the identity you created in me from the beginning. I don't want to live from what is false but from the truth. I want to be clothed in your righteousness and not in any garments that cover who I'm really meant to be. The calling and destiny you have for me can only come forth from my authentic self. Have your way in this. In Jesus' name, amen.

QUESTIONS AND EXERCISES

1. Reflect on the following statements. If you are in a small group, share what you personally believe about the concept of loving yourself.

   - If I love myself better, I will be able to love others better.
   - If I love myself less, I will have a greater capacity to love others.
   - Caring for our own hearts isn't selfish; it's how we begin to love.
   - If I expect myself to perform and be perfect, I will undoubtedly expect others to do the same.

2. As a Christ-follower, ponder the difference between being in a community of "nice" people versus in a community of "real" people. At this time in your life, which one do you prefer? And why?

3. Can you identify where a lack of self-love and self-acceptance has negatively impacted relationships in your life?

4. What roles did you learn to play growing up?
   a. Responsible one/little adult/"good" child
   b. Trouble-maker/scapegoat
   c. Lost child/quiet child
   d. Little husband/little wife
   e. Clown/comedian

5. Which traits below describe you? Have you tried to step away from any of them? Do you see them as "just who you are" or as issues for God to heal and restore?
   a. Perfectionist
   b. People pleaser
   c. Martyr
   d. Caretaker
   e. Stuffer
   f. Doer
   g. Fixer

NOTES

CHILDHOOD BUILDING BLOCKS

For an answer Jesus called over a child, whom he stood in the middle of the room, and said, "I'm telling you, once and for all, that unless you return to square one and start over like children, you're not even going to get a look at the kingdom, let alone get in. Whoever becomes simple and elemental again, like this child, will rank high in God's kingdom. What's more, when you receive the childlike on my account, it's the same as receiving me."
(Matt. 18: 2–5)

Overview

In session 3, we focus on the stages of childhood and how the wounding during these growing up years gets carried into our adult lives. We explore the critical building blocks of trust

THE MISSING COMMANDMENT: LOVE YOURSELF

and identity and how, when they are compromised, a breach occurs which carries throughout all of life.

Reading Assignment

In the book *The Missing Commandment: Love Yourself*, read Chapter 3, "Come as a Child" (pp. 31–42), and Chapter 6, "Foundational Building Blocks: Trust and Identity" (pp. 85–95).

Video Session

On the teaching DVD, watch session 3: "Childhood Building Blocks" (8:29). You can use the narrative script below for your own review and reflection. Highlight or make notes of any parts that stand out to you.

Building Blocks

Now, some of you may feel some resistance to what we are going to say next, but if you want to know what's hindering you from loving God, self, and others, you are going to have to look closely at your foundation—your childhood. Look at it this way: if you had a building inspector coming to inspect the house you wanted to purchase, one of the most crucial places he would begin checking is its foundation.

For it is on this foundation that the rest of the structure has to be supported. What use would an inspection be without first checking the foundation?

So let's take a look at this visual demonstration of the importance of your childhood—your foundation—where life patterns and habits and identity begin.

Nesting Dolls: The Child Within

[Denise shows a set of five "nesting dolls": a doll within a doll within a doll, etc.] Let me show you these nesting dolls, which are a great visual of how important it is to heal all the parts inside us. These nesting dolls just keep coming apart, and inside each one is another little child. Inside this one is another one, and another one, and an even tinier one—all the way back to the newborn. In life, you could take it even further back to the womb.

When we showed these to one of our clients, she was really impacted by the littlest one. She said, "It's like that one—even *that* one—still matters."

Let's say it *doesn't* matter. It doesn't matter that she wasn't planned, that she was the wrong sex, that it was a bad time financially for her mom and dad, that it would have been better for her parents if she had never been born. Let's just forget about that one.

Unfortunately, that was when she was supposed to be developing trust—by the time she was one year old: trust that would allow her to hold her heart open to love for her entire life. If trust is not developed then . . . you just have to do without.

And so, let's see . . . there's this one, around the age of two or four—that toddler, preschool age where we learn whether or not we're OK. So either I am me and I am OK, or I am me and I am *not* OK: if you knew the real me, you wouldn't like me. So I am going to learn to be good, or I'm going to learn to grow up before my time. Or maybe I don't want to remember this time, because that's when my dad left or when my grandfather fondled me. But that doesn't matter. That was so long ago.

So now if I decide not to deal with this little one, then I have lost even more than the ability to trust and hold my heart open to love (including God's love; maybe I can't even trust him). I have also lost the part of my life where my identity is formed, and hence, my destiny. This child part of me— this part that should feel special, loved, and accepted; this part where I should feel OK about being me—let's say I don't want this part either.

This next one, maybe seven, nine, ten—I was doing pretty well at school. I had some good friends there. But you know, Dad was gone a lot, and when Dad was home, he drank a lot and didn't seem to connect with me. Mom was upset at Dad and confided in me. She tried to make things OK when Dad was angry. I just stayed in my room when that happened. It could have been worse. I'm sure others had it worse than me.

Then there's the teenager. Oh, well, what should I say? Maybe I was more rebellious, insecure—experimenting with alcohol and sex. Maybe I like that person a little bit—at least the part that did well in school or in sports. I just can't accept all of her. I'd rather not remember some of the times.

Here I am as an adult person, and all I've got left are these pieces. And now I'm supposed to function like a whole person, and I'm really just part of a person. So maybe I've just decided to forget my past totally, and I'm kind of left empty. And the Father in his great love says, "You know, Denise, *I—love—all—of—you*. And there is not one part that I do not like. There is not one part that I cast off. There is not one part that I don't want to reclaim for my own."

God wants us to love and accept *every* part of us— the hurt parts, the rejected parts, the neglected parts, the empty parts, the shamed parts, the abused parts, the angry parts. He says, "I will make you into a whole being. There is not any part of you that I cast off, but I call every part home—home to my heart, to my love, to the way that I have created you."

And only when we come to that realization can we become all we were meant to be. Integrated into oneness. Whole—in him.

The Breach

Did you catch the first building block of your life? It's trust. Trust is established in the first year after birth, when we mirror what our mother is feeling. So how she feels about me determines how I feel about myself. And then, right after that building block—built right on top of trust—is our identity, our perception of self. By the age of four, a child internally decides whether "I am me and I am OK" or "I am me and I am *not* OK." If you're not OK, this is the beginning of what we call *toxic shame*.

By the age of six or seven, most of a child's personality is formed. Only major events like divorce, abuse, or the death of a loved one will further shape the child's personality. And if there is a breach in the foundation of trust, it will cause a break all the way through life.

PRAYER

Father, you know everything about me and yet you do not reject any part of me. Lord, I am choosing to stop and let you show me all of myself—and please share with me if there are younger parts of myself that I have ignored, rejected, or abandoned—if there are parts of me that I do not welcome home like you do.

Lord, you say that you want me to live from a place of wholeness and not from a place of being fragmented within. You say that unity among your people is very important. I want that unity to start within me. Reveal what needs to be healed and help me to trust you in this. In Jesus' name, amen.

QUESTIONS AND EXERCISES

1. Two early building blocks in a child's development are trust and identity. If trust is established, we are able to hold our hearts open to love. With identity, we establish a core sense that "I am me and I am OK." What deficits can you identify in these areas of yourself? What struggles do you experience in your adult life and in relationships with others, including God, that would suggest a breach in either the trust or identity stages of development?

2. Quiet yourself and ask God to show you a picture of yourself as a child before the age of eight. What do you see? What do you see yourself doing? Complete the following statements:
   - When I picture myself as a child, I want to _____.
   - Is this child happy? Why or why not?
   - Do you like this child? Why or why not?
   - How do you feel about this child living inside you (like the nesting dolls)?
   - How do you think the Father feels about this child?

3. Ponder this statement: "The biggest impact on how we see God is not our knowledge of the Scriptures but the representation or misrepresentation of God that we saw mirrored in our parents." How true is this statement in your own life experience?

NOTES

THE EMPTY PLACES

"Prepare for GOD's arrival! Make the road straight and smooth, a highway fit for our God. Fill in the valleys, level off the hills, smooth out the ruts, clear out the rocks. Then GOD's bright glory will shine and everyone will see it. Yes. Just as GOD has said."
(Isa. 40:3–5)

"The water I give will be an artesian spring within, gushing fountains of endless life."
(John 4:14)

[The man in my vision] brought me back to the entrance to the Temple. I saw water pouring out from under the Temple porch to the east. . . . He walked to the east with a measuring tape and

*measured off fifteen hundred feet, leading me
through water that was ankle-deep. He measured
off another fifteen hundred feet, leading me
through water that was knee-deep. He measured
off another fifteen hundred feet, leading me
through water waist-deep. He measured off
another fifteen hundred feet. By now it was a river
over my head, water to swim in, water no one
could possibly walk through.*

*. . . [He told me . . .] "Wherever the river flows, life
will flourish. . . . Where the river flows, life abounds."
(Ezek. 47:1, 3–5, 8–9)*

Overview

In session 4, we begin with God's original design for us. Using water bottles, we then demonstrate how wounds of both abuse and lack create empty places in us—whether from the presence of harmful things in our childhood that we should not have experienced or from the absence of good things in our childhood that we should have experienced, such as love, affection, protection, and belonging.

We also share "Katie's Story: Letter to the Child Within," written to her previously disliked and unaccepted child inside. Katie movingly and powerfully displays her inner wrestling when confronted by the Father who wants her to love herself like he does.

Reading Assignment

In the book *The Missing Commandment: Love Yourself*, read chapter 4, "What Does God Feel—About Us?" (pp. 43–63) and chapter 7, "Shields Up: The Ways We Protect Ourselves," (pp. 105–121).

Video Session

On the teaching DVD, watch session 4: "The Empty Places" (9:40). You can use the narrative script below for your own review and reflection. Highlight or make notes of any parts that stand out to you.

The Water Bottles

We have discussed childhood wounding and the great impact it can have on us. Let me show you what I mean.

[Jerry picks up the first of two full water bottles.] Let me use this water bottle to illustrate. Let's say that it represents us as a child. Inside this bottle is water, which, as you can see, is pretty much filled to the top. It represents what God placed in us right from the very beginning—what he designed for us to have. Now let's say that as we start our life and move into childhood, some things start to happen.

When a child is overtly wounded, the damage is often easier to identify. Let's say there was physical abuse [Jerry pours out some water with each example]—the belt that left welts or the spanking that was over the top. Or maybe there was some form of sexual abuse, whether it was overt abuse or finding Dad's pornography. Or maybe a mother or father used their child as an emotional confidante or a companion; that is abusive too.

But you know, abuse doesn't have to be physical or sexual. It can also be verbal or emotional—hurtful words such as, "You're so stupid," or, "I can't believe you would do that," or, "What's wrong with you?"

Words don't even have to be spoken. A slap on the face, a gesture, or a mere look can communicate shame perfectly. We end up with a child who no longer has what God desired and designed for him or her—a child with a deficit that will carry into adult life. [Jerry shows that the bottle is now only one-quarter full.] It will affect that person's relationships at work, at home, and even with God.

Now this next point is critical: It is not only the *direct* harm that comes to a child that does lasting damage—it is also what *didn't happen* or was *lacking* when the child was growing up.

So let's look at this *other* bottle. [Jerry picks up the second full water bottle.] Here again is our beginning—starting out with all God designed for us. But let's say your mother was not very nurturing [Jerry again pours out water with each new example], that you didn't receive much affection and care from your parents, or maybe you never got words of affirmation or praise, or maybe you never heard "I love you." Maybe you didn't have a sense of belonging, or you felt like an outcast— that you just weren't a part of the family.

The result is that the child doesn't know that he or she was loved, special, precious, significant, deserving of the very best.

Maybe Dad traveled a lot. Maybe he just wasn't emotionally available when he was at home. Or maybe there was a lack of spiritual or emotional guidance that God designed you to receive. How about limits? Maybe there weren't any limits placed on you—appropriate limits, limits that communicate love.

Later on in life, we may wonder, "Why am I struggling with fear?" "Why am I struggling with depression?" "Why am I so irritable and angry?" But we just can't put our finger on anything, because "nothing really happened." And that's the point: nothing overt happened that would explain why we're having a problem. Instead, we experienced a *lack* of what we needed. What we were given by our caregivers was less than what God said we needed and deserved to make us whole.

As with overt wounding, these kinds of wounds will cause us to function from a deficit [Jerry shows the bottle, now just one-quarter full], and we will have problems in our closest relationships and with God.

So what does God say about this? "Well, you know, that was unfortunate. I wish it wasn't that way, but just pull yourself up by your bootstraps and press through"? Or does he say, "You'll just have to learn to cope with that"? Or does he say, "It wasn't that bad. A lot of people have it worse than you"?

I don't think so. In fact, I know he doesn't say such things, because that isn't his heart. He is a redeemer and a restorer, and he asks us to invite him into these places of hurt. When we do that, he will begin to pour back into us what we needed. [Jerry begins filling one bottle of water back to the top.]

Why does he do this? Because he loves us so much, and he knows that we need everything he designed for us in order for us to fulfill the calling and destiny he placed within us from the very beginning.

Katie's Story: "Letter to the Child Within"

Dear little Katie,

I am writing to you to tell you some things that were never made clear to you and address insecurities and lies that were never addressed. You need to know, firstly, that you are OK and loved by God just the way you are. There is nothing you could change about yourself that would make him love you any more or any less.

You do not need to change yourself to be accepted by others. You are free to be yourself. You are not weird. You are not awkward. You are not annoying. You do not need to perform to obtain love and approval. Just the way you are is good enough for God. You need to know that it is OK to cry and get upset. It does not make you a brat or dramatic. You do not need to stuff your emotions or hide your problems; they do not make you a bother. You are not responsible for the happiness of those around you. It is not your job to fix other peoples' problems. You do not have to fix your problems by yourself. You have a Father in heaven that wants to help you through your toughest situations.

I'm sorry I was so critical of you. I'm sorry I did not love you. I'm sorry I believed the lies that you are annoying, bratty, ugly, not good enough, and weird. You were given the gift of a sensitive heart, and I'm sorry I did not embrace that. I'm sorry I taught you to suppress your emotions, and when they became too much, I'm sorry I turned my anger toward you. Just know that you are OK. You are precious in God's eyes, and He loves you very, very much.

Love, Katie

PRAYER

Father, sometimes it seems like I shouldn't be looking at myself and my own needs but should be focused more on others. Yet I know that there are things in me that interfere with this desire to love you and love others more completely. I know that you came to heal broken hearts and set people free, and I am one of those people. There are places in me that needed more love when I was young, and they have affected me negatively. Open my heart to accept the truth and take down any self-protection that keeps me captive in some way to those wounds. I want all that you have for me. In Jesus' name, amen.

QUESTIONS AND EXERCISES

1. Reread the narrative script "The Water Bottle." In your childhood, what things happened to you directly that should *not* have happened? What things were *lacking* in your childhood, things you needed more of than you actually received? How has all this impacted you? If you do not know, ask the Father for his truth.

2. Shaming messages can be spoken as well as silently communicated through a look, a gesture, or a frown. What shaming messages do you remember from growing up?

3. How would your life be different if those messages were silenced?

4. To emphasize the strength of affection John felt from Jesus, *The Message* translates John's reference to himself as "the one Jesus loved dearly" (John 13:23). Does this seem offensive or prideful to you on John's part to write about himself that way? Could you imagine that the Father would be delighted if you described yourself this way? Why or why not?

5. Ask yourself which of the following you believe and live from: "Nothing can separate me from the love of God," or (from the church marquee down the road), "Get Right or Get Left." Is there any difference in what you believe in your head versus your heart? Or do you hold a different standard for what you believe for others versus what you believe for yourself?

6. Is the thought of feeling God's feelings for you personally a new revelation? How difficult is it for you to believe that God cares so much about you that he feels your sadness, despair, disappointment, and joy right along with you?

7. Picture this: You are the "one lost sheep" in Matthew 18:12–13. You are first on God's list. (In God's math, it is as if each one of us is the only lost sheep). You are not merely one of the ninety-nine. Your needs are important. Your wants. Your cries. Your tears. Your pain. Your shame, fear, hopes, dreams, identity, calling, destiny—all of these are important to God. Do you feel any resistance to any particular part of this list?

8. Write a letter to a younger part of yourself like Katie did. You can find several other examples in our book *The Missing Commandment: Love Yourself.*

NOTES

THE JOURNEY
BACK HOME

*The Spirit of GOD, the Master, is on me
because GOD anointed me. He sent me to preach
good news to the poor, heal the heartbroken,
announce freedom to all captives, pardon all
prisoners. GOD sent me to announce the year of his
grace—a celebration of God's destruction of our
enemies—and to comfort all who mourn.*

*. . . They'll rebuild the old ruins, raise a
new city out of the wreckage. They'll start
over on the ruined cities, take the rubble left
behind and make it new.*
(Isa. 61:1–2,4)

Overview

In session 5, we invite you to join us on the healing journey back to your home of origin. We share how somewhere in our development, we often end up veering off on a different set of tracks than God's original design for us. God invites us to join him in healing our past so we can realize his dreams for our lives. The session concludes with "Dean's Story" and how his healing journey is restoring his heart, his relationships, and his destiny.

Reading Assignment

In the book *The Missing Commandment: Love Yourself*, read chapter 5, "Going Back to Go Forward" (pp. 65–84).

Video Session

On the teaching DVD, watch session 5: "The Journey Back Home" (6:20). You can use the narrative script below for your own review and reflection. Highlight or make notes of any parts that stand out to you.

The Railroad Tracks
One way to visualize the healing process is to think of a set of railroad tracks. The tracks symbolize the path God intended for us from the point we were placed on this earth. They represent his perfect will for our lives.

Now, somewhere along the way, as we start growing up and life begins to happen around us, we diverge off onto a different set of tracks, other than the ones God intended.

When we finally realize our life is headed the wrong way, the only choice we have is to turn around and let God take us back to the place where we grew up: back to our family of origin. It is human nature to want to find a quick fix—to want to just jump the tracks and get on with life. But God likes his plan better than ours. His plan rebuilds trust, heals broken places, and tears down the walls we built to protect ourselves. The journey home is not easy. It takes time. It hurts. But it is necessary. Along the way, the Father will point out signs and billboards of our past, some of which we may not even remember. He asks us to be willing to see whatever he wants us to see and feel whatever he wants us to feel—no more and no less than he says. He asks us to be willing to see the truth about what happened to us growing up that is still affecting us in some way today. The Father invites us to move back onto the original tracks of our true identity so we can fulfill our destiny—his dreams for us.

Dean's Story

When I began my healing journey, I had no idea that the events of my childhood had laid a foundation for who I would become as a man. I never realized how much my relationship with my earthly father distorted my view of God—and I didn't feel a deep heart connection with either of them.

When I was a child, I learned not to depend on anyone but myself. I learned not to trust the adults in my life who seemed to make arbitrary rules with no explanations—kind of like, "Because I said so." When I grew up, I began to see God in the same way I saw my caregivers. I couldn't trust him because he also seemed unpredictable and arbitrary. I was unable to feel a deep heart-connection with God, and I actually didn't even know there was more of a relationship with God available to me.

I was gifted with artistic creativity, but I was discouraged from pursuing art as a career path. I was told, "You will never earn a living that way." So I began to pursue worldly success and formed a belief that God would not value me unless I was performing and doing something of significance. My gift of creativity was "nice" but was not of great importance if I wanted to be successful.

I had already learned to be self-reliant and to not trust others regarding decisions for my life. I pursued success as a means to validate my worth as a man, a husband, and a father. And in the midst of my striving, God showed me there was a deep void inside me that especially showed up in my closest relationships. I was very logical and practical but not emotionally available.

In the healing process, I have learned that my emotions are important, that a connected heart is life-giving to me and others. I have learned that vulnerability is no longer something to avoid in order to protect myself from getting hurt. I now realize that vulnerability is key to having real and meaningful relationships. I am learning to trust God more and more and know that I am valuable to him not because of what I do, but because I am his son.

PRAYER

Father, sometimes I feel pretty alone in this journey of life. And sometimes I feel like I am only experiencing a fraction of the life you designed for me to have with you. Lord, am I on the path that you desired for me from the very beginning? I invite you to show me where I am on this journey. If this is not the path that you planned for me and you want me to experience more of your healing to be able to walk on a different path, I give you permission to reveal this to me. If

THE MISSING COMMANDMENT: LOVE YOURSELF

you need to take me backward in order to go forward into more life and wholeness, I say yes to that. I know there will be pain involved in that journey home, but I am willing. All I ask is that you walk back with me. I can't do this without you, and I don't want to even try. I need you. Thanks for loving me enough to heal me. In Jesus' name, amen.

QUESTIONS AND EXERCISES

1. Are you game for the journey back to your home of origin? Do you feel any resistance to God's invitation?

2. In what ways does the fruit of your life or the struggles in it indicate that you may have veered onto a different set of tracks from what God intended for you at the beginning?

3. Consider these wise counseling sayings: *You can't heal what you don't feel. Feel it to heal it. Grieve it to leave it. What God reveals, he plans to heal.* How have these sayings been experienced in your life?

4. How vulnerable, open, and safe do you feel in your closest relationships, including your relationship with God? What has hindered you?

5. From his childhood, Dean learned
   - to rely on himself
   - that God values him only when he is doing something of significance
   - that, like his parents, God is arbitrary
   - that God cannot be trusted

   What do you think lessons like these cost Dean—or you?

N O T E S

WHO'S DRIVING YOUR CAR?

Then he told them what they could expect for themselves: "Anyone who intends to come with me has to let me lead. You're not in the driver's seat— I am. Don't run from suffering; embrace it. Follow me and I'll show you how. Self-help is no help at all. Self-sacrifice is the way, my way, to finding yourself, your true self. What good would it do to get everything you want and lose you, the real you?"
(Luke 9:23–25)

Overview

In session 6, we share how the unhealed child parts within us can drive our adult behaviors, feelings, and relationships. We ask you to consider a vital question: "How old is the child driving my adult emotional car, and is this child inside old enough to have a license?" We conclude this session with a discussion of the different faces of toxic shame and provide examples for self-evaluation.

Reading Assignment

In the book *The Missing Commandment: Love Yourself*, read chapter 6, "Foundational Building Blocks: Trust and Identity" (pp. 95–104) and chapter 8, "Shame and the Lies We Believe" (pp. 123–141).

Video Session

On the teaching DVD, watch session 6: "Who's Driving Your Car?" (6:09). You can use the narrative script below for your own review and reflection. Highlight or make notes of any parts that stand out to you.

Who's Driving Your Car?

Jerry and I have a unique question that we often ask in counseling: "How old is the child who is driving your emotional car, and is he old enough to have a license?"

The point of the question is this: many times our adult patterns of relating and behaving and feeling are driven on the inside by a much younger self.

For example, Patricia remembers her father coming home from overseas when she was a young girl. She climbed up onto his lap and couldn't love on him enough. She was so happy he was home. Then something traumatic happened: her daddy took her arms off from around his neck and put her down on the floor away from him. Patti walked away with tears running down her face, and no one noticed.

Let's park the car here for just a minute and let us ask you another question: What was the Father feeling when that happened to Patti? Devastation? Pain? Anger? Sorrow? All the above? I know that I felt my heart sink. Did God's too?

Without Patti realizing it, her heart put up a wall to protect herself from ever being hurt again—a wall that now hinders her intimacy with her husband as well as with God.

So we ask the question, "How old is the child who is driving the adult Patricia's emotional car, and is she old enough to have a license?"

* * *

Bob grew up in a very legalistic home. In church, if he even moved, his dad hit him on the head. Early on, Bob learned to conform, to be perfect, to be good, quiet, nice, and never to show anger. He told us the inscription on his tombstone would be, "He was just a nice guy." That's it. Not even his name.

Bob said, "My dad broke my spirit. I stopped being who I really was, and I learned to be who he wanted. That way I could look good and keep the peace."

But then Father God showed Bob how he saw him: a warrior with a heart like David, full of fierce passion and desire. Bob's destiny was to live fully alive in his God-given identity, but instead he had learned to deaden his feelings so he could survive.

So, "How old is the child who is driving the adult Bob's emotional car, and is he old enough to have a license?"

* * *

Sandy grew up in an alcoholic home where both of her parents were addicted. She describes herself as just a stray on the street, orphaned. She recalls that she was treated like a grown-up and left in charge of her parents from the time she was a small child. When she was very young, she locked up the house at night because her mom and dad were passed out, drunk.

Today Sandy believes God sees her, but he doesn't care about her. All she wants in her life is for someone to come and take care of her. That cry is from an empty place in her heart.

So, "How old is the child who is driving the adult Sandy's emotional car, and is she old enough to have a license?"

Toxic Shame

All of these stories have a common theme: toxic shame. This is the type of shame that is not about something I do—it is about who I *am*. As we grow up, our shaming self-talk tends to become quite a believable set of lies:

> "I'm the problem. When something is wrong, it's my fault."
> "Even when I do my best, it is never good enough. I can never meet the standard."
> "No one will ever love me just for me."
> "I am a disappointment to God."

Oddly, while some shame-based individuals may be critical and hard on themselves, others will respond by being critical and overpowering of others. Their belief system sounds more like,

> "I will always be in control."
> "I will never be weak or be vulnerable."
> "I will always be right and insist on my own way."

One thing both of these types of shame have in common is, they both come from a wounded heart. They are trying to get their needs met in an unhealthy way, and both of these types of individuals desperately need to learn to love themselves.

PRAYER

Father, I want to be whole. I don't want my life today to be driven by any wounded part in me that is reacting to toxic shame and is still crying out for love. Lord, if there is any core shame within me that hinders my ability to love you, myself, and others, I ask you to reveal it to me. I ask this so that I can ultimately walk in the freedom that you desired for me when you sent your Son Jesus in order to restore all things—including me. I want to be free of the lies that still affect me—even the ones that I haven't seen up to this point but are still there. I know that if you reveal this type of shame in me, it is already your plan to ultimately heal me from its effects. Please have your way in me. Thank you for your love. In Jesus' name, amen.

QUESTIONS AND EXERCISES

1. Ask yourself the following questions about how toxic shame manifests in you. (If you can take a risk, ask someone close to you how they would answer these questions about you).
   - Do I become defensive with others?
   - Am I critical of myself and/or others?
   - Is my self-talk negative, condemning, and merciless?
   - Am I a perfectionist?
   - Am I performance-driven, a "human doing" versus a human being?
   - Do I fear closeness and intimacy, craving it yet fleeing from it?
   - Do I isolate physically or emotionally, shutting down or stuffing my feelings?
   - Do I have difficulty identifying or expressing feelings?
   - Am I a people-pleaser, longing for approval and recognition?
   - Do I have difficulty trusting others, including God?
   - Am I sensitive to criticism, even when it's constructive?
   - Do I have difficulty making decisions?
   - Do I find myself trying to prove I am OK by working harder or doing more?
   - Do I struggle with addictive behaviors?

2. How do you relate to the controlling side of toxic shame? Ask yourself these questions:
   - Is it hard for me to admit I am wrong and say I am sorry?
   - Do I need to be right in order to feel better about myself?
   - Do I always have to be in control?
   - Can I be weak and vulnerable with others?

3. How far back do you think these shame reactions began?

4. What examples can you identify in your adult life where your emotions or reactions are really those of a younger inner child? "How old is this child who is driving the adult's emotional car, and is he or she old enough to have a license?" Ask God to show you where these reactions originated in your childhood.

NOTES

"I AM ME AND I AM OK"

You'll get a brand-new name straight from the mouth of GOD. You'll be a stunning crown in the palm of GOD's hand, a jeweled gold cup held high in the hand of your God. No more will anyone call you Rejected, and your country will no more be called Ruined. You'll be called Hephzibah (My Delight), and your land Beulah (Married), because GOD delights in you.
(Isaiah 62: 2-4)

Overview

In session 7, we help you take a look at your negative self-talk and the ungodly beliefs (lies) that you hold against yourself. We address the masks you may wear in order to belong, to feel accepted, and to be loved. We conclude with an invitation for you to join the Father on a journey to heal your brokenness, so that you can walk in the freedom of God's original plan for your life. Only then will your heart be ready to love whom God loves—YOU.

Reading Assignment

In the book *The Missing Commandment: Love Yourself*, read chapter 9, "Good Grief: From Self-Forgiveness to Self-Acceptance" (pp. 143–159) and chapter 11, "Be Good to You + Be God to You = Loving Who God Loves" (pp. 177–186).

Video Session

On the teaching DVD, watch session 7, "I Am Me and I Am OK" (2:42). You can use the narrative script below for your own review and reflection. Highlight or make notes on any parts that stand out to you.

Katie's Story Continues: The Chalkboard

So now we come back to the question: Can I love others when I don't do a good job of loving myself? How well, then, am I loving others? The answer: No, I can't. Especially when I am just doing whatever I can to be liked, accepted, and appreciated by others; when I need their affection, attention, and approval; when I can't have anyone mad at me... in short, when I can't let anyone see the real me.

When you look at me, the person you see is a mask, a fabricated self—so once again I have abandoned my real self, rejected myself, and shamed myself. If I don't measure up enough for myself, I will never be able to internalize and believe the love and care that God and others have for me.

[While Denise is speaking, Katie is writing these words on the chalkboard.]

I am ...	I am ...
unwanted	inadequate
unloved	invalidated
unimportant	insignificant
unworthy	invisible
unaccepted	insecure

Now God is inviting you to go on a healing journey—where the story of your past no longer controls you—when your past is no longer stuffed down inside, buried alive. We allow ourselves to go back to our childhood—our foundation—so we can then move forward on the original set of tracks God intended for us. We learn what happened to us: both the harmful things and the absence of good things that we deserved and needed. We learn that what happened matters—that some of our behaviors and patterns of relating are being driven on the inside by a much younger self who doesn't have a license.

And because we matter to God and he is right with us, with his arm around us, we courageously press in. We risk. We discover. We grieve. We grow. We heal.

[Katie erases all of the prefixes to the words and writes in the caption below.]

I am . . .	I am . . .
wanted	**adequate**
loved	**validated**
important	**significant**
worthy	**visible**
accepted	**secure**

I Am Me and I Am OK

More Good News

We learn that God calls us to love what he loves—that we must love ourselves and like ourselves as much as God loves and really likes us. The missing commandment will not be missing in our lives anymore. Then we will be truly free to love God and turn around and love others—just like we love ourselves.

PRAYER

Father, thank you for your process of redemption and restoration—big words that have a simple meaning: that I am important enough to you that you made a way to find me, heal my heart, and bring me to a new place. Thank you that you sent your Son Jesus to heal my broken heart and set me free from the things that have kept me bound in some way. Your Word says that "it is for freedom that Christ has set us free" (Gal. 5:1). I stand in that freedom and I refuse to accept anything less.

I know that I am unable to do anything without your help, including living from a place of freedom and life, so I ask you to help me continue to love and accept myself and live from your heart. Help me to love you, myself, and others in the way you intended. In Jesus' name, amen.

QUESTIONS AND EXERCISES

1. Which words on the list below are now or have been on your "chalkboard?"

   unwanted   inadequate
   unloved   invalidated
   unimportant   insignificant
   unworthy   invisible
   unaccepted   insecure

2. When the prefixes (*un* and *in*) to the words above are erased, the lies and shaming words are transformed into the words of God's truth for us. What truths do you need God to reveal that were hidden under the lies you believed?

3. Standing in front of a mirror, look directly and deeply into your eyes and speak the following affirmations. These are truths that agree with how God our Father feels toward you—truths that make him smile.
   Repeat this exercise until you can believe all of it—because it agrees with God's heart for you.
   - I love you, _____ (your name).
   - I am fearfully and wonderfully made.
   - I am a precious treasure to God.
   - I am the one Jesus loves dearly.
   - I am the apple of God's eye. He celebrates the day I was born.
   - I was on his mind from the beginning of time.
   - He calls me by name— _____ —and says, "You are mine."
   - There is nothing I could ever do to make him love me more.
   - There is nothing I could ever do to make him love me less.
   - I am special.
   - I am a daughter/son of the King.
   - I am a treasure and a delight.
   - God loves me, and I love me too.

4. Which of these affirmations are more difficult for you to receive and believe for yourself? Is it easier to believe these affirmations for others? Explain.

5. What does this statement mean to you? "The Father wants you to be free to *be*come, and to come to *be*, all that he created you to *be*."

6. Re-read the prayer at the end of this session aloud. Add your own hopes and desires for your ongoing healing journey.

NOTES

CONCLUSION

Thank you for being our audience as we have shared our understanding of what the Father has planned for you from the beginning. We are blessed to have had you walk with us on this healing path. It is a journey that is worth the trouble and worth the risk.

In closing, we wish to share with you one more time a basic yet profound truth: God is with you. Throughout your journey to healing, wholeness, and life, be assured of this:

God is here. Right now. On your side. At your side. His arm is around you. He is actively seeking to help you and will never, *ever* leave you. He is looking with you at your struggles, your questions, your wrestlings. It is you and he together. He is an ever-present help in trouble. He is passionate about YOU—the delight and pride of his life.

FROM THE AUTHORS

Thank you for taking the time to read and process our book, teaching DVD, and companion study guide. If you have been impacted by what we have shared, would you be willing to share these resources with others? You could

- Recommend our book to people in your church, school, workplace, class or small group.
- Recommend our book on Facebook, Twitter, Pinterest, or your blog post.
- Purchase a copy for someone you know who would benefit from this message.
- Subscribe to our blog for more articles, testimonies, upcoming promotions, and new titles at **www.fathersheartmin.wordpress.com**.

NOTES

NOTES

NOTES

NOTES

NOTES

NOTES

NOTES

NOTES

NOTES

NOTES

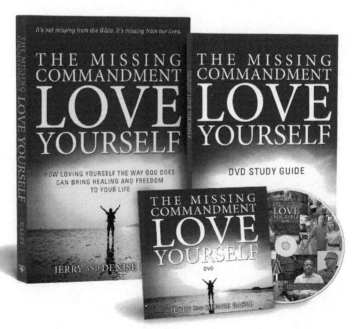

Made in the USA
Middletown, DE
16 January 2017